To Gloria, Theresa, and Martin.
From my hands to your hands.
                    T.R.

ISBN 0-590-45835-3

Text copyright © 1985 by Bill Martin Jr.
Illustrations copyright © 1987 by Ted Rand.
All rights reserved. Published by Scholastic Inc., 730 Broadway, New York, NY 10003, by arrangement with Henry Holt and Company, Inc.

12 11 10 9 8 7 6 5 4 3 2 1   2 3 4 5 6 7/9

Printed in the U.S.A.   09

First Scholastic printing, October 1992

Here Are My Hands

By Bill Martin Jr. and John Archambault
Illustrated by Ted Rand

SCHOLASTIC INC.
New York Toronto London Auckland Sydney

Here are my hands
for catching and throwing.

Here are my feet
for stopping and going.

Here is my head

for thinking and knowing.

Here is my nose
for smelling and blowing.

Here are my eyes

for seeing and crying.

Here are my ears
for washing and drying.

Here are my knees
for falling down.

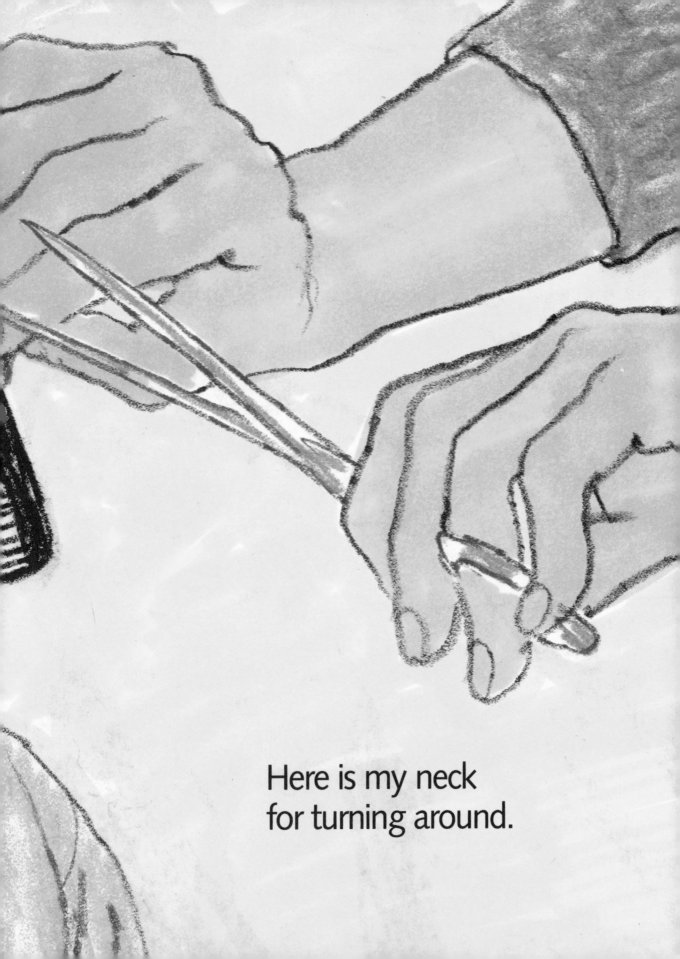

Here is my neck
for turning around.

Here are my cheeks
for kissing and blushing.

Here are my teeth

for chewing and brushing.

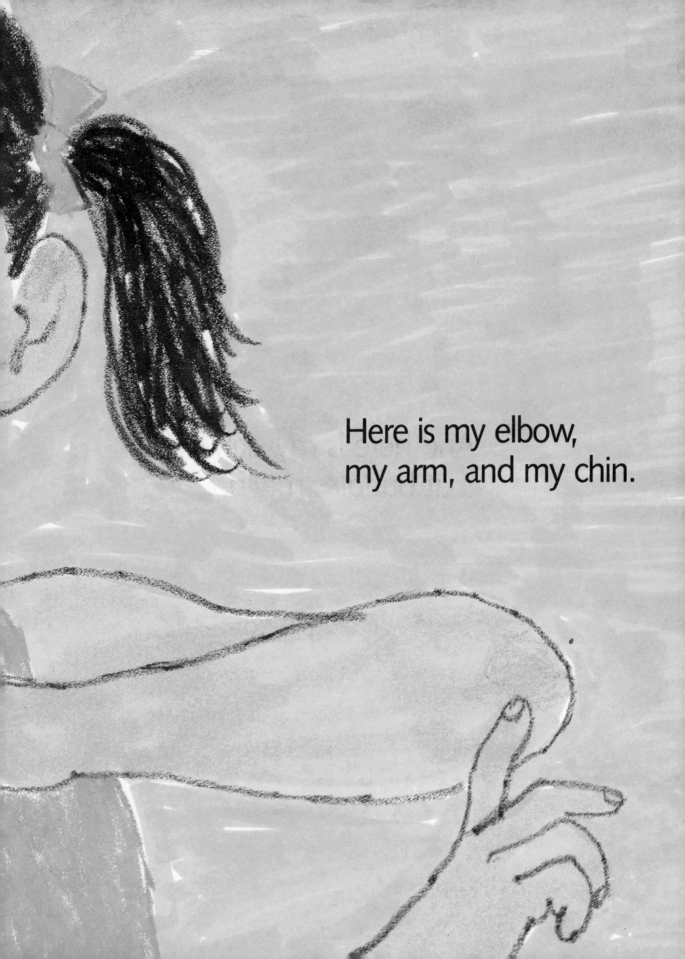

Here is my elbow,
my arm, and my chin.

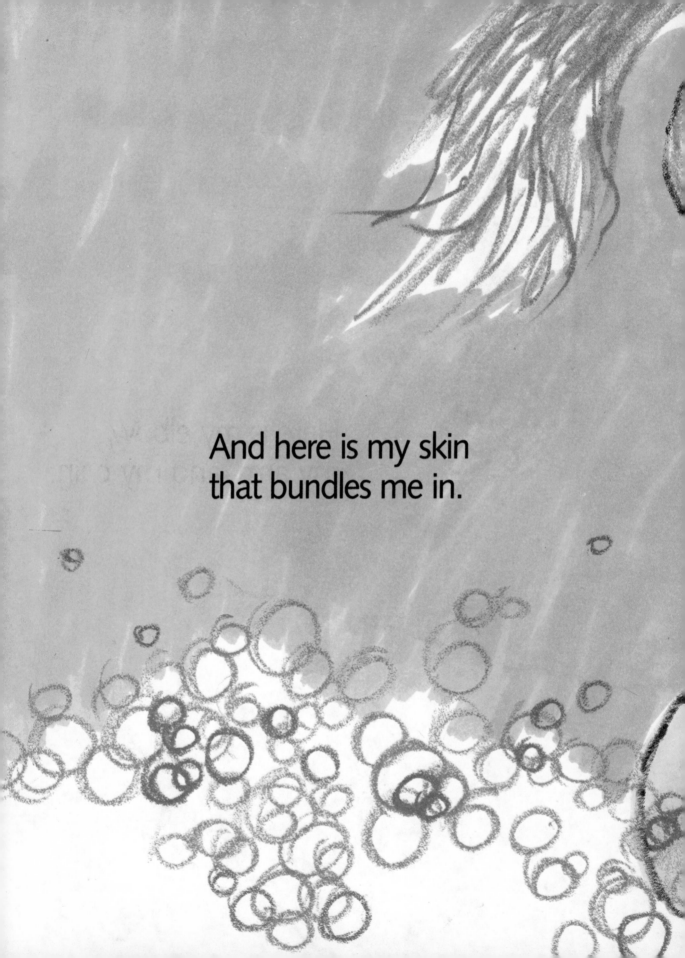

And here is my skin
that bundles me in.